Reycraft Books
55 Fifth Avenue
New York, NY 10003

Reycraftbooks.com

Reycraft Books is a trade imprint and trademark of Newmark Learning, LLC.

Story and illustrations ©2010 by Hsin-Yu Sun.
Originally published by Hsin Yi Publications, Taipei, Taiwan.
All rights reserved.

This edition published by arrangement with Hsin Yi Publications, Taipei.

Educators and Librarians: Our books may be purchased in bulk for promotional, educational, or business use. Please contact sales@reycraftbooks.com.

This is a work of fiction. Names, characters, places, dialogue, and incidents described either are the product of the author's imagination or are used fictitiously. Any resemblance to actual persons, living or dead, is entirely coincidental.

Library of Congress Control Number: 2020909959

ISBN: 978-1-4788-7029-6

Printed in Dongguan, China. 8557/0720/17279

10 9 8 7 6 5 4 3 2 1

First Edition Hardcover published by Reycraft Books 2020

Reycraft Books and Newmark Learning, LLC support diversity and the First Amendment, and celebrate the right to read.

REYCRAFT
B O O K S

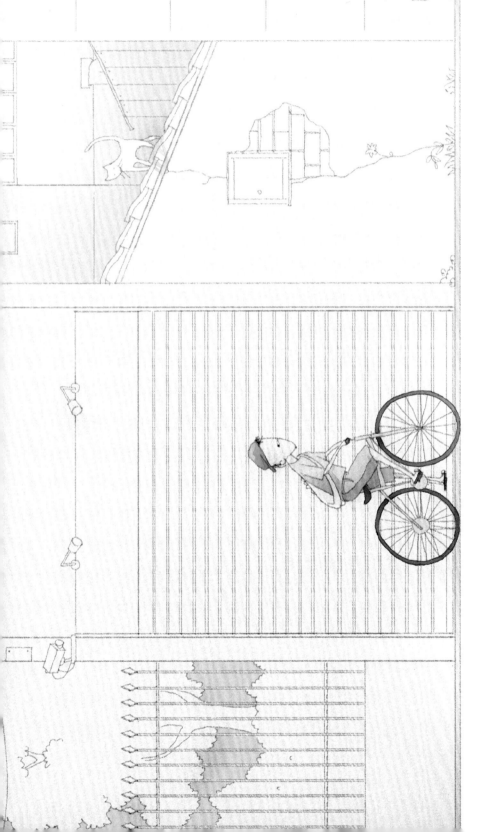
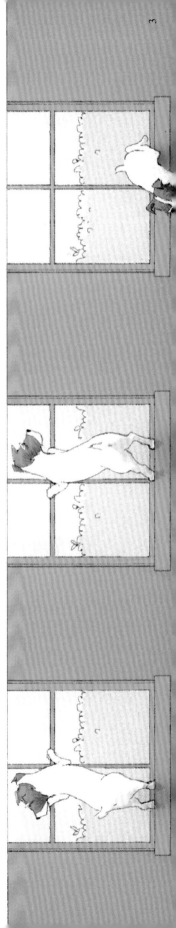

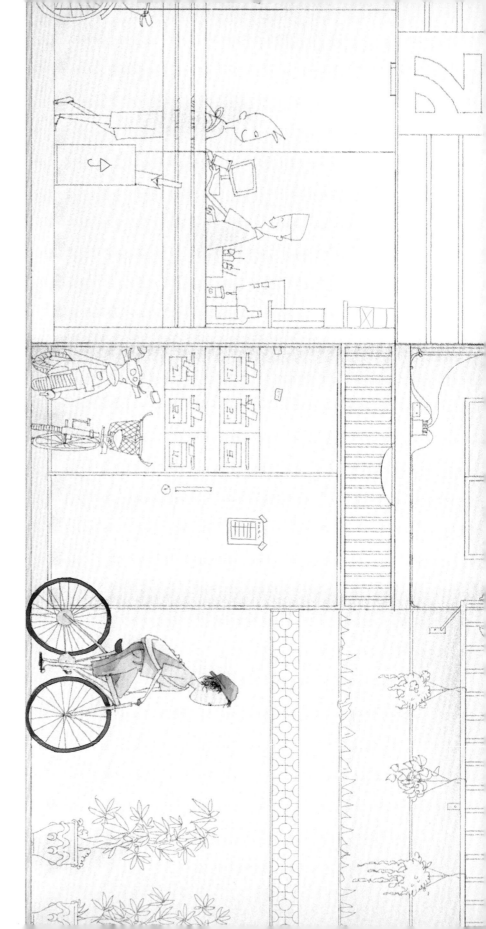

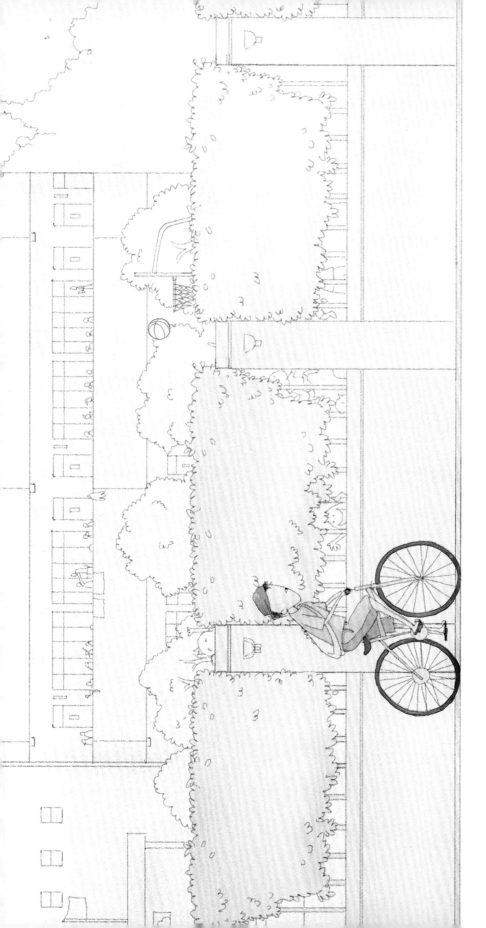

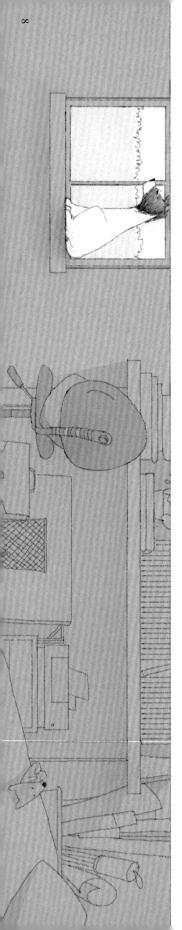

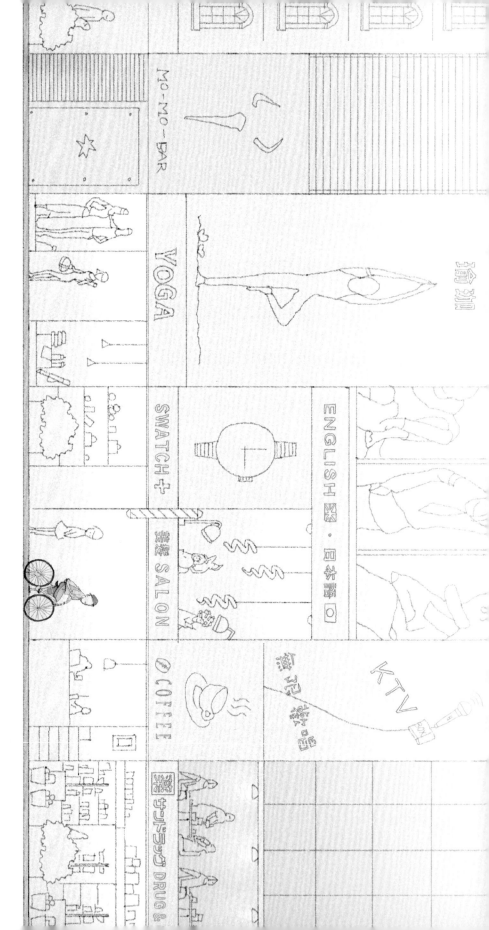

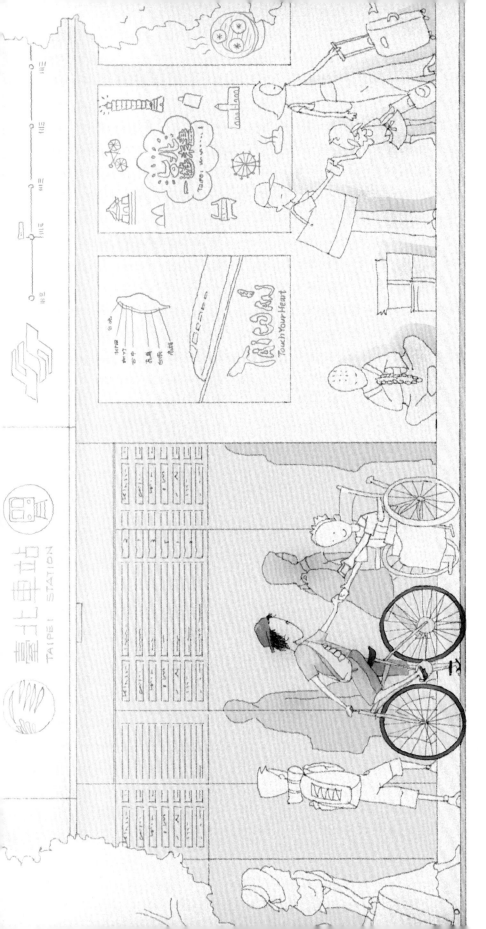

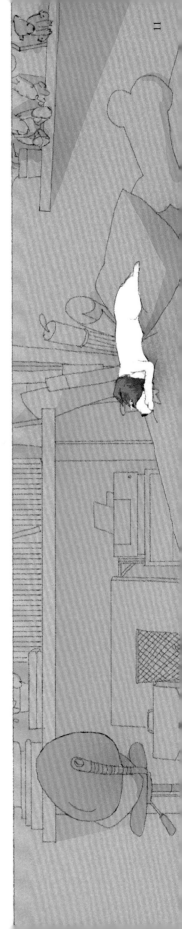

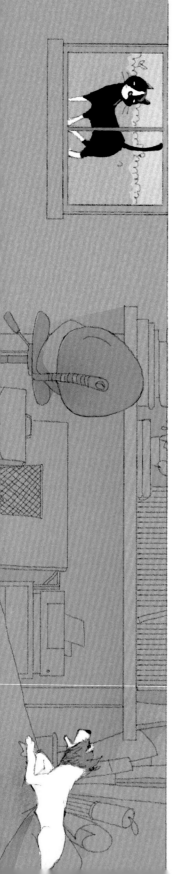

南京板鴨

小籠包

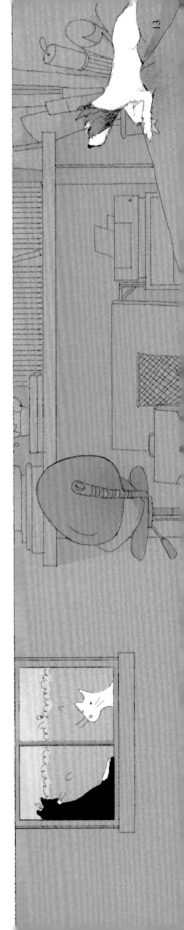

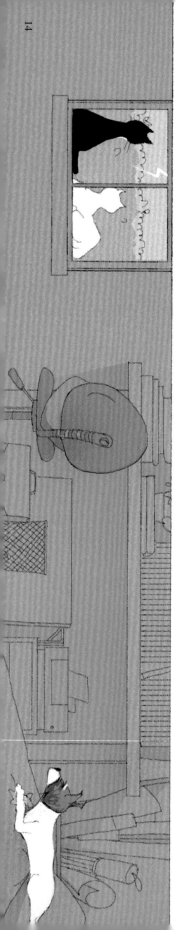

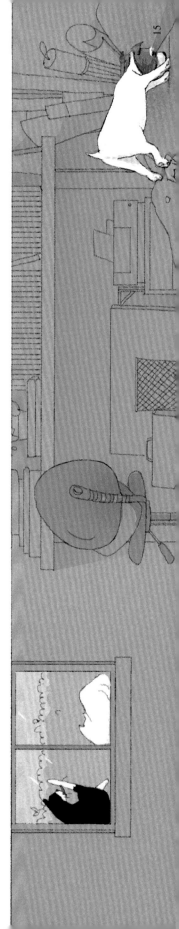

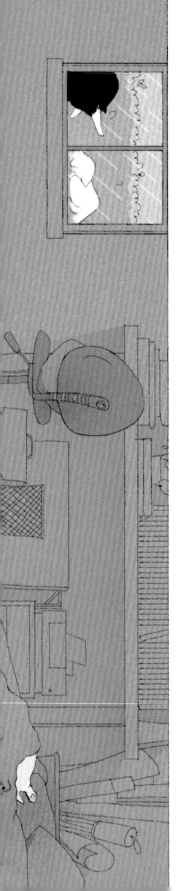
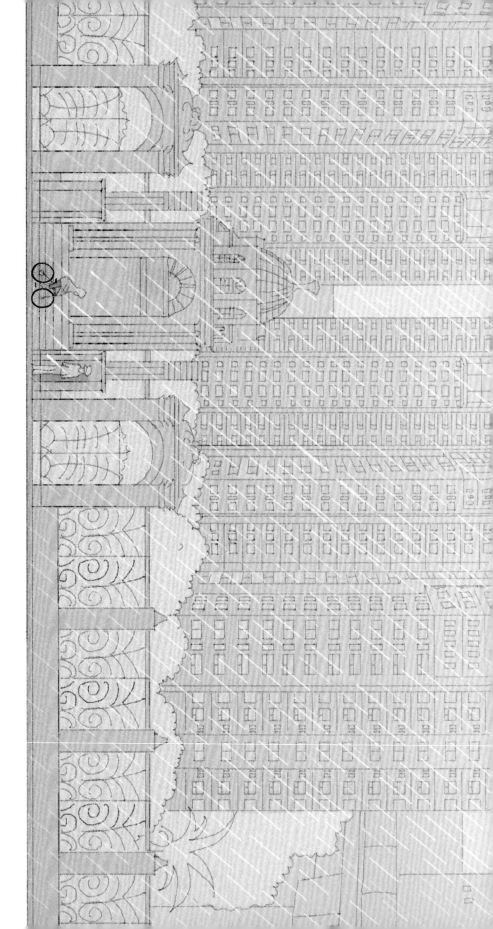

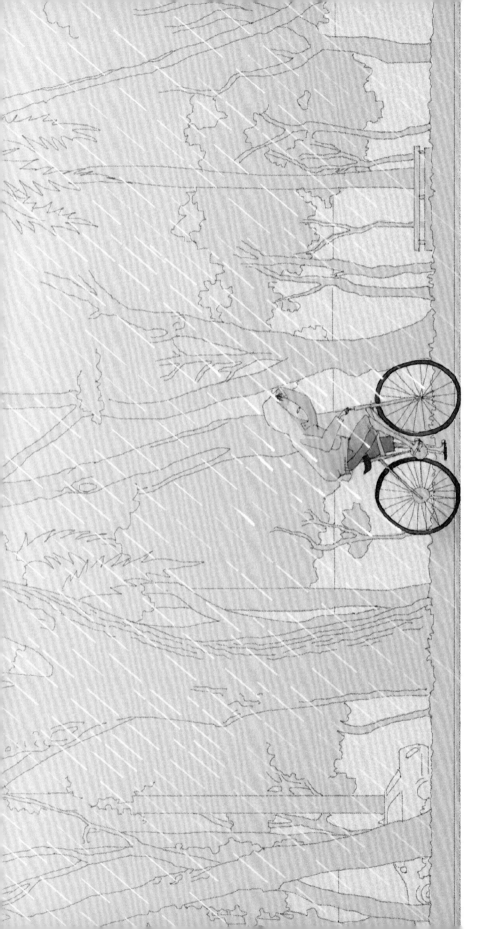
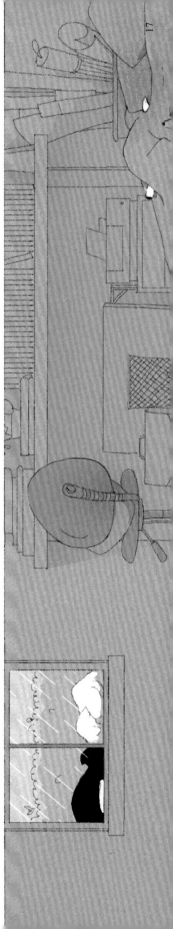

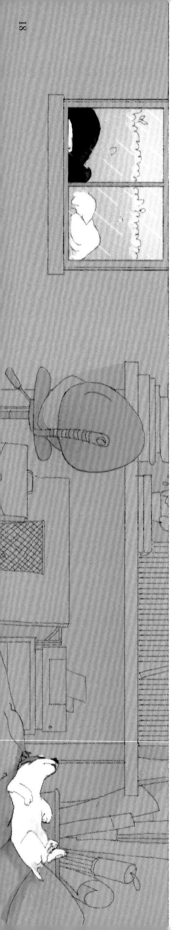

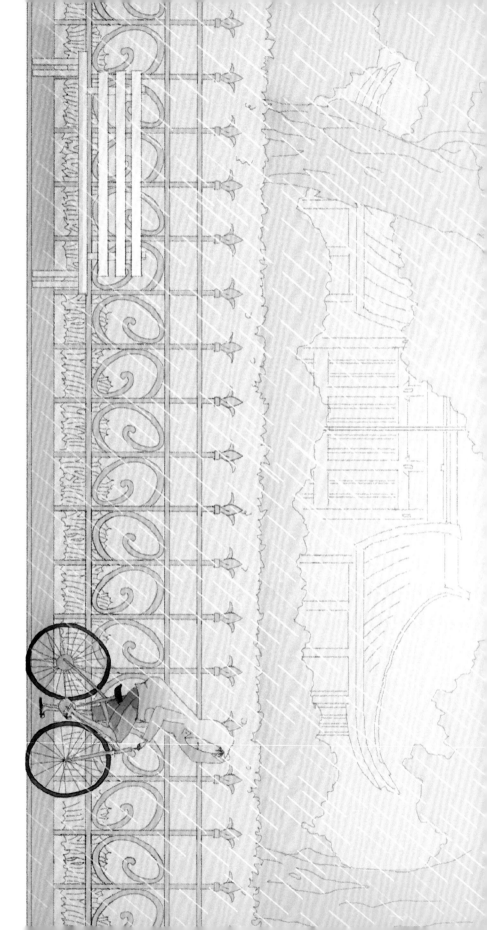

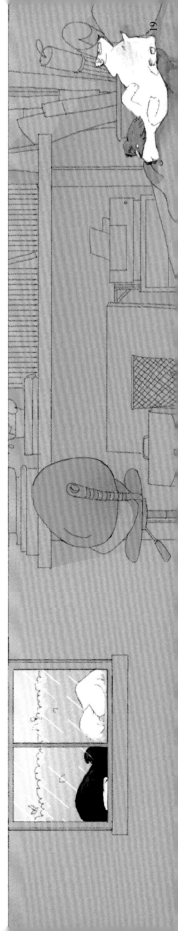

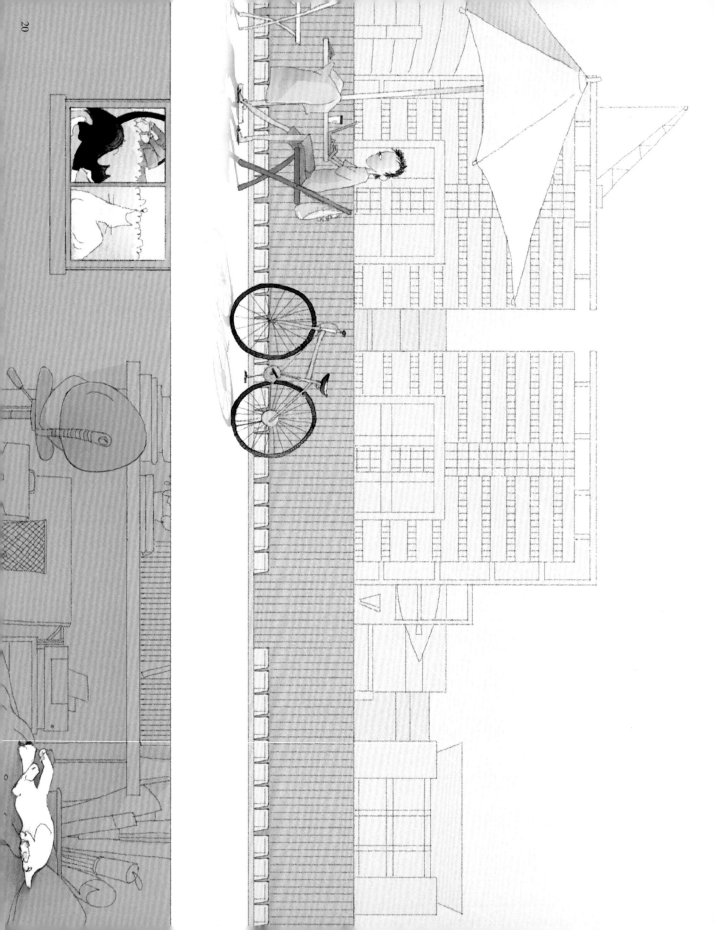

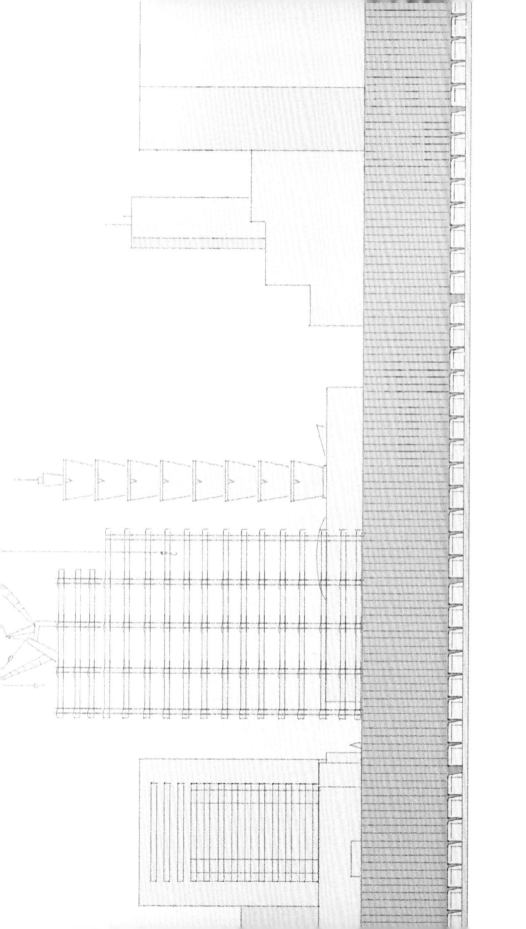

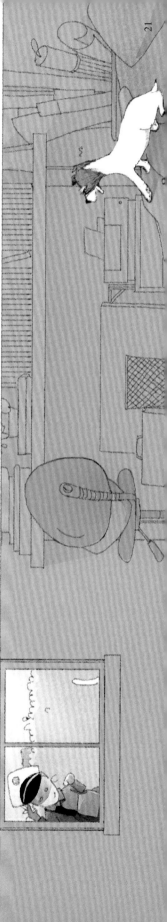

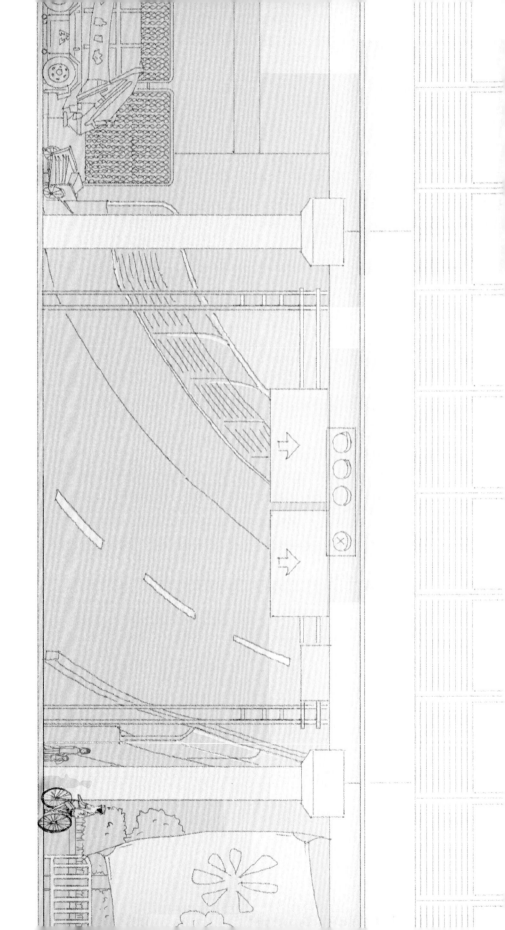

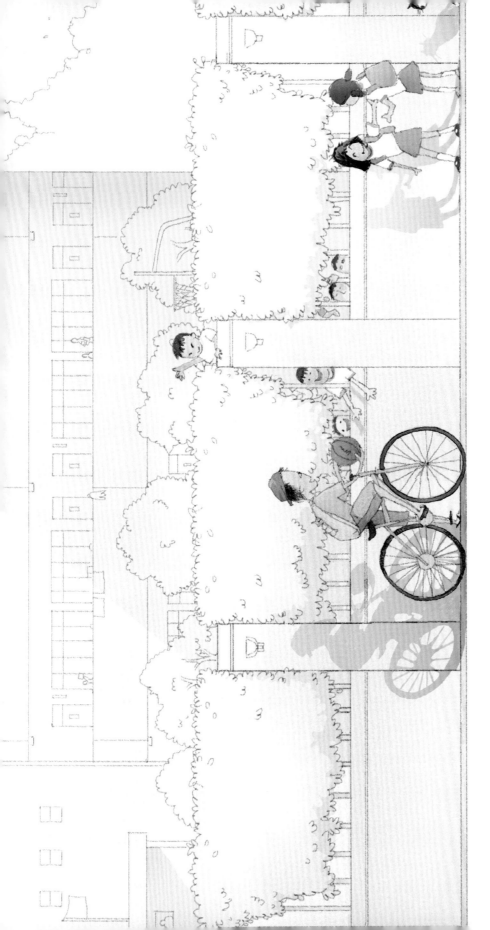
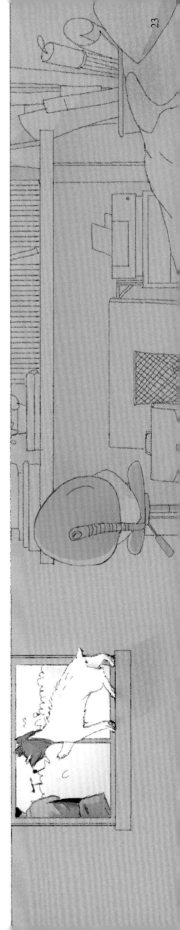

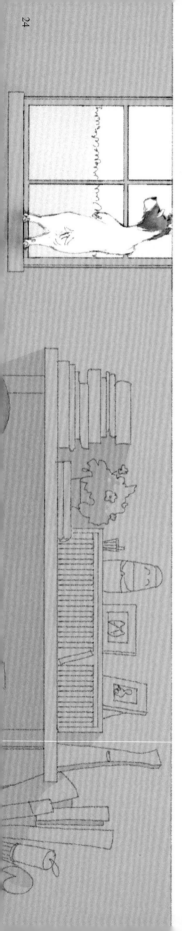

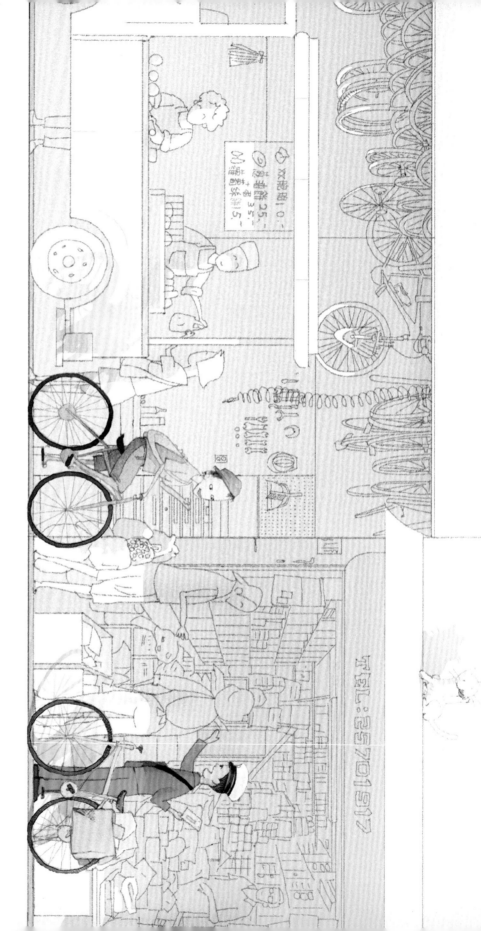

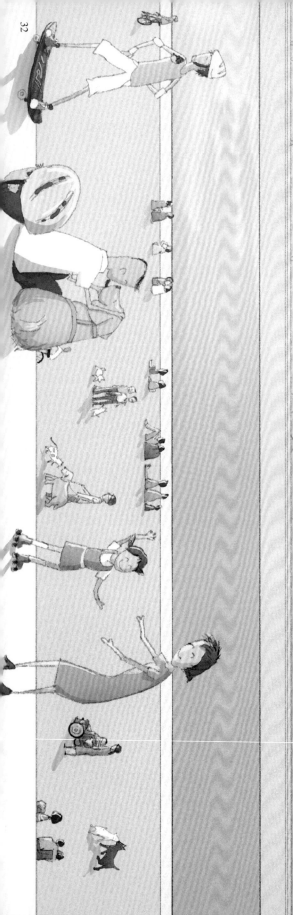
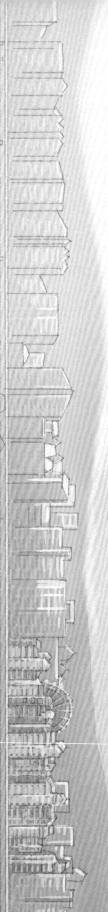

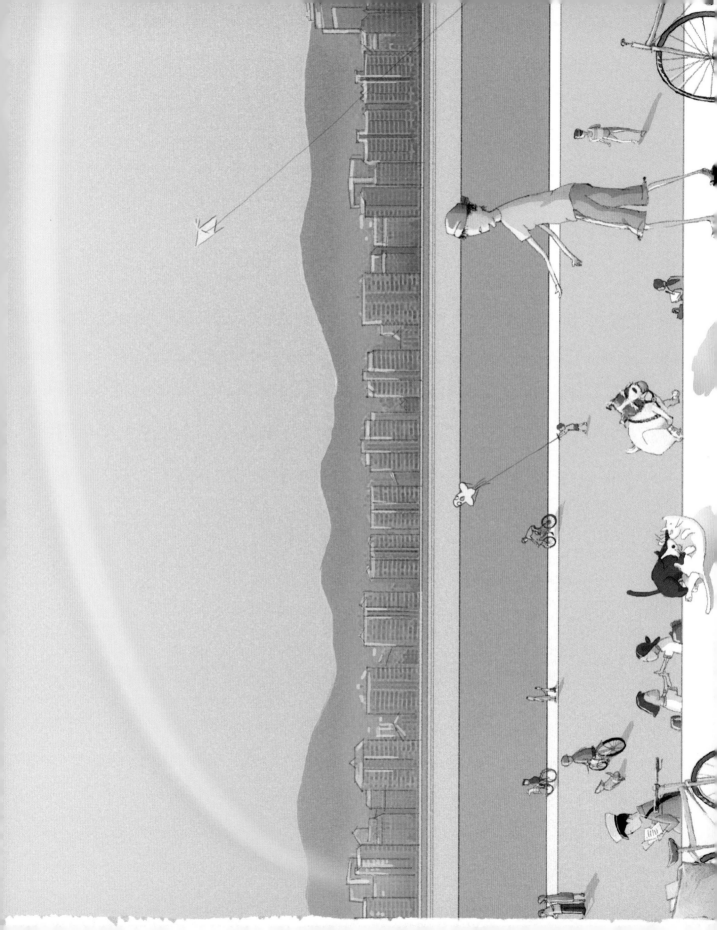